What Do I Need?
¿Qué necesito?

by Deborah Schecter

ISBN: 978-1-338-70289-7
Illustrated by Anne Kennedy
Copyright © 2020 by Deborah Schecter. All rights reserved.
Published by Scholastic Inc., 557 Broadway, New York, NY 10012

10 9 8 7 6   68   23 24 25 26/0

Printed in Jiaxing, China. First printing, June 2020.

ⅢSCHOLASTIC

I need a table.

Necesito una mesa.

I need a chair.

Necesito una silla.

I need a blanket.

Necesito una manta.

I need a pillow.

Necesito una almohada.

I need a snack.

Necesito una merienda.

I need a flashlight.

Necesito una linterna.

I need a friend!

¡Necesito una amiga!